HARPIST   Joanne Wicks   grade 7
                                    examiner

Violin
Specimen
Sight-Reading
Tests

ABRSM Grades 6–8

from 2012

Notes

1 In the exam, candidates will be given a short interval of up to half a minute in which to look through and, if they wish, try out any part of the sight-reading test before they are required to perform it for assessment.

2 The fingering and bowing marks given in this book (as well as in the exam tests) are for guidance only; examiners will not assess whether they are observed.

Published by ABRSM (Publishing) Ltd, a wholly owned subsidiary of ABRSM

Sarah's Lullaby

Fire Dance

AB 3597

Minuet

Up and Away

Melodic Etude

5

Dawn Song

6

AB 3597

Time to Tango

Sea Shanty

Busy Day

9

Melancholy

10

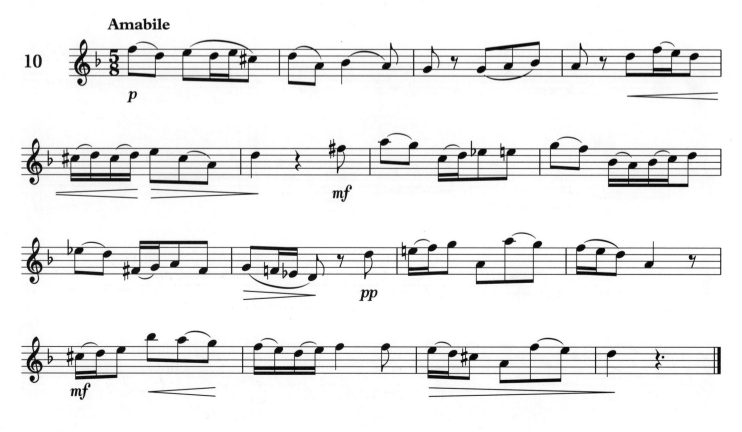

Country Walk

Sailor's Song

The Hunt

Humoresque

Musical Box

Graceful Aria

Reflection

17

A Walk in the Park

18

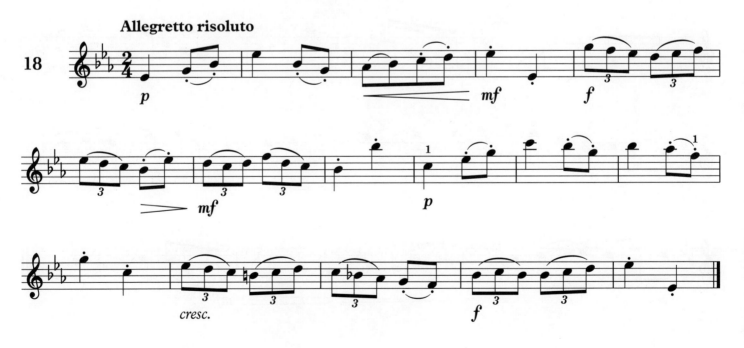

AB 3597

Romance

Afternoon at the Fair

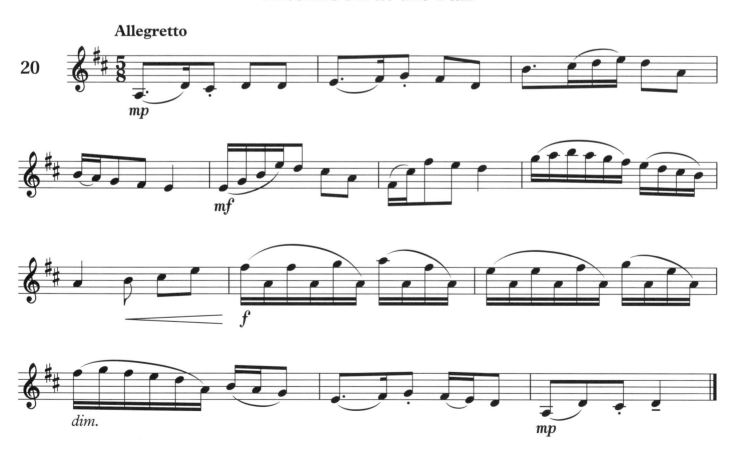

Bavarian Dance

Circus Tricks

Fairytale Castle

Summer Song

Over the Far Hills

Gigue

Blues in 7

Lament for Summer

Homage to Bach

Elegy

Romanian Dance

Busy All Day

Sorrowful Song

Sonatina

Lament

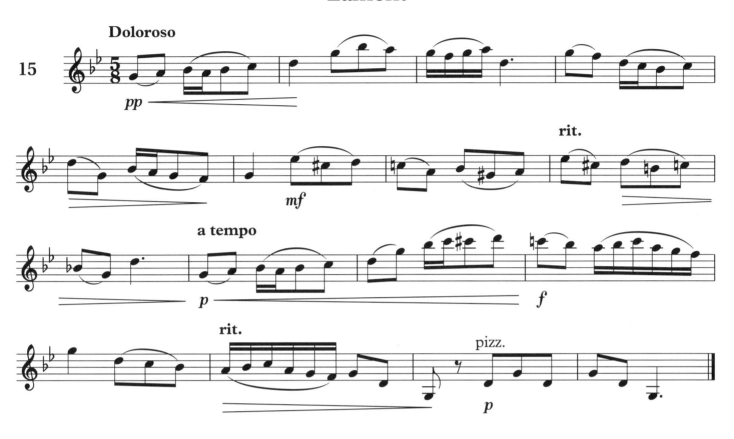

Folk Dance

Meditation

By the Stream

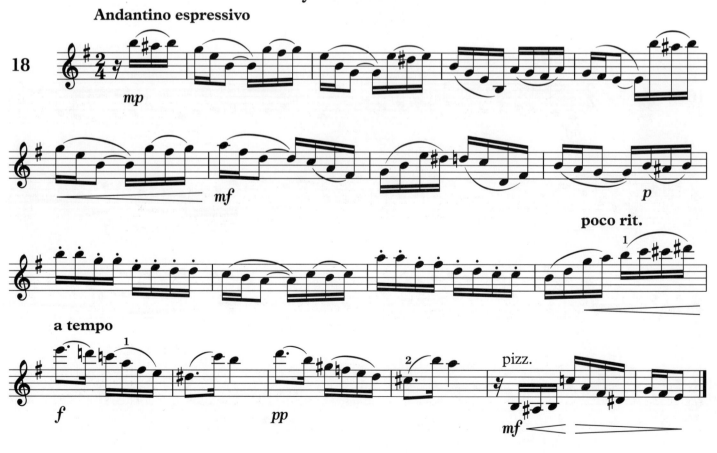

Cityscape

The Green Hills

Regrets

Invention

Witches' Dance

Toy Soldiers

The Old Clock

Sarabande

Romance

Frogs

Shall We Dance?

Long Ago

AB 3597

The Adventurer's Escape

In the Ballroom

Lullaby

Hungarian Dance

Concertino

Sunrise

Song without Words

Blues for Charlie

Folk Dance

Butterflies

Music origination by Julia Bovee and Katie Johnston
Printed in England by Caligraving Ltd, Thetford, Norfolk